FUNNY-SIDE UP

A Tasty Joke Book

Stephen Hillenburg

Based on the TV series *SpongeBob SquarePants*® created by Stephen Hillenburg as seen on Nickelodeon®

ISBN-13: 978-0-545-07724-8
ISBN-10: 0-545-07724-9

12 11 10 9 8 7 6 5 4 3 2 1   8 9 10 11 12 13/0

Printed in the U.S.A.

First Scholastic printing, November 2008

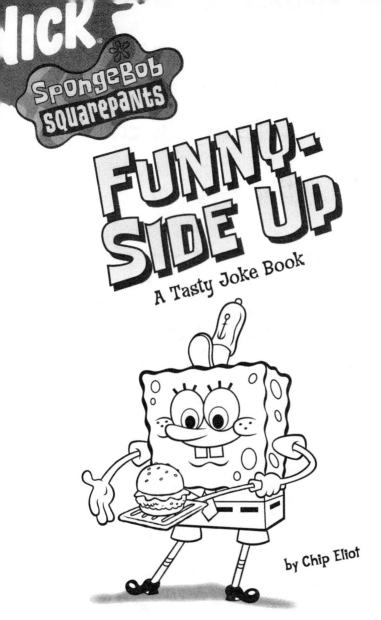

NICK

SpongeBob SquarePants

FUNNY-SIDE UP

A Tasty Joke Book

by Chip Eliot

SCHOLASTIC INC.
New York Toronto London Auckland Sydney
Mexico City New Delhi Hong Kong Buenos Aires

Are you ready to navigate your way through the yummy SpongeBob SquarePants joke zone?

Okay, let's roll . . .

How does SpongeBob like his eggs?

Funny-side up.

Why did Patrick hold a stone and a Krabby Patty bun to his ears?

He wanted to hear some rock and roll.

SpongeBob: Patrick, will you join me in a cup of ice-cold lemonade?

Patrick: No, I don't think there's room for both of us.

Why did SpongeBob bring a tub of margarine to Mrs. Puff?

He was trying to butter her up.

Why couldn't the egg lend Patrick any money?

Because it was broke.

What happened when SpongeBob ate one plate of spaghetti too many?

He went pasta point of no return.

KRUNCH! KRUNCH! KRUNCH! KRUNCH! KRUNCH!

Why did Mr. Krabs want a job at the bread factory?

Someone told him he'd make a lot of dough.

Mr. Krabs: Once when I was shipwrecked, I lived on a small can of beans for a week.

SpongeBob: That's amazing! I'm surprised you didn't fall off.

Mr. Krabs: Try some of my seaweed salad. It will put some color in your cheeks.

Sandy: Who wants green cheeks?

Patrick: I'll have a Krabby Patty, Mr. Krabs.

Mr. Krabs: With pleasure.

Patrick: No, with tartar sauce.

What is Squidward's favorite fruit?

Sour grapes.

Squidward: Mr. Krabs, how do you make a gold-medal Krabby Patty?

Mr. Krabs: Easy. Just add fourteen carrots.

Patrick: Why is my Krabby Patty all squished?

SpongeBob: You told me you were in a hurry and that I should step on it.

Why does Squidward complain whenever he eats?

He likes to whine and dine.

Mrs. Puff: I'd like a Krabby Patty, and make it lean.

SpongeBob: Which way?

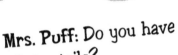

Mrs. Puff: Do you have lobster tails?

Mr. Krabs: Yes, once upon a time there was a little lobster . . .

Mrs. Puff: What fruit can you find everywhere in the ocean?

Pearl: That's easy. Currants.

Why did SpongeBob study all the old grease stains left on the grill at the Krusty Krab?

Mrs. Puff said he should learn about ancient Greece.

Why did Patrick swallow a bunch of coins?

His mother said it was lunch money.

What did SpongeBob say when he saw the brand-new griddle at the Krusty Krab?

"Ah, the grill of my dreams!"

Pearl: What kind of cup can't you drink out of?
Patrick: A cupcake.

Why did Patrick toss a peach into the air?

He wanted to see a fruit fly.

Mrs. Puff: What is this fly doing in my alphabet soup?

Mr. Krabs: Learning to read?

Patrick: This Krabby Patty is way too rare. Didn't you hear me say well-done?

Squidward: Yes, I did. Thank you very much.

KRUNCH!

KRUNCH!

KRUNCH!

KRUNCH!

KRUNCH!

KRUNCH!

What do sailors like to eat for lunch in Bikini Bottom?

Submarine sandwiches.

SpongeBob: Patrick, why have you been staring at the carton of orange juice for three hours?

Patrick: It says, "Concentrate!"

How did Mr. Krabs learn to cook?

He took ten greasy lessons.

Patrick: SpongeBob, can you fix dinner?

SpongeBob: I didn't even know it was broken.

Mr. Krabs: How was your chicken soup?

Sandy: It was fowl.

Plankton: Do you take orders to go?

SpongeBob: Yes.

Plankton: Well then—GO!

Why did SpongeBob put a chicken into his garden?

He was trying to grow eggplant.

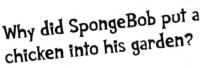

Why did SpongeBob take a Krabby Patty bun to a fashion show?

He wanted it to be a roll model.

What happened when Pearl won the Bikini Bottom hot-dog-eating contest?

She was declared the wiener.

Sandy: How long will my Krabby Patty be?

Mr. Krabs: It won't be long. It will be round.

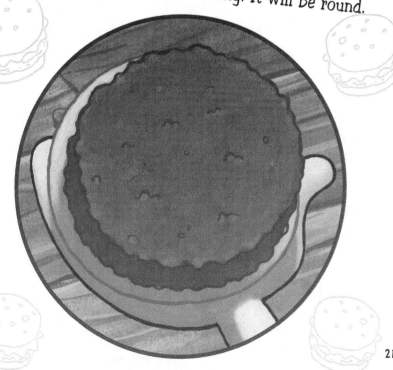

Sandy: What kind of shoes can you make from bananas?

Patrick: I don't know.

Sandy: Slippers.

Who brings candy to all the good boys and girls in Bikini Bottom in the spring?

The Oyster Bunny.

Why did Sandy put sugar under her pillow?

She wanted to have sweet dreams.

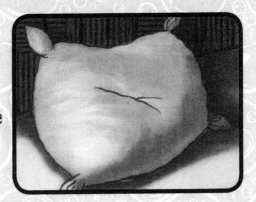

Why did Patrick quit his job at the doughnut factory?

He was sick of the "hole" business.

Pearl: Why is it impossible to starve on a beach?

Sandy: Because of all the sand which is on it.

What does King Neptune like to drink?

Royal tea.

Why did Patrick put a frankfurter in the freezer?

He wanted a chilly dog.

What does a pirate have in common with corn that costs a dollar?

Both are a buck an ear.

SpongeBob: Did you hear about the egg that laughed itself silly?

Patrick: No, what happened?

SpongeBob: It cracked up!

SpongeBob: What do astronauts put on their sandwiches?

Sandy: Launch meat.

KRUNCH

Where can you see hamburgers dance?

At a meatball.

KRUNCH

KRUNCH

Patrick: What is your stew like today?

Mr. Krabs: Just like last week's, only a week older.

KRUNCH

Why do clams and mussels not like to share?

Because they're shellfish.

Pearl: Did you hear the one about the banana that got sunburned?

Patrick: No.

Pearl: It began to peel. Did you hear the one about the lunchmeat?

Patrick: No.

Pearl: It's a bunch of baloney. Did you hear the one about the stale cookie?

Pearl: Yeah, it was really crummy.

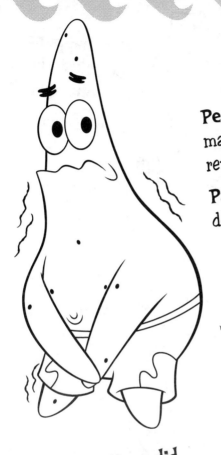

Pearl: What did the mayonnaise say to the refrigerator?

Patrick: Please close the door. I'm dressing.

What kind of lettuce did they serve on the *Titanic*?

Iceberg.

What happens when you ask shellfish personal questions?

They clam up.

What kind of fruit do sailors like most?

Naval oranges.

Mrs. Puff: What fruit conquered the world?

SpongeBob: Alexander the Grape.

SpongeBob: What do you call fake spaghetti?

Squidward: Mock-aroni.

If a tomato and a lettuce had a race, which would win?

Lettuce, because it's always a head.

SpongeBob: What vitamin should you take to improve your vision?

Squidward: Vitamin See.

Why did Patrick take a dozen eggs to the gym?

He wanted them to get some eggs-ercise.

Why did Patrick throw sticks of margarine out the window?

He wanted to see butter fly.

What do you call SpongeBob when he sings and drinks soda at the same time?

A pop singer.

What's the smallest room in the world?

A mushroom.

What does SpongeBob's daily diet consist of?

Three square meals.

Why does Patrick like to talk to a cornfield?

Because it's all ears.

What sandwich is always scared?

A chicken sandwich.

SpongeBob: What do you give a lemon when it needs help?

Sandy: Lemon-aid.

What did Patrick say to the pickle?

"You're dill-icious!"

Why did Patrick want a job in the salt and pepper factory?

He was hoping to find seasonal work.

What do sea monsters eat?

Fish and ships.

SpongeBob: Why are tomatoes the slowest vegetable?

Mr. Krabs: They're always trying to ketchup.

Mrs. Puff: I asked you to write a composition on cheese yesterday. You didn't hand anything in. Why not?

SpongeBob: The tip of my pen kept getting clogged with cheese.

SpongeBob: Mr. Krabs, do you know how to make a lobster roll?

Mr. Krabs: Sure. Just take a lobster to the top of a hill and push!

Mr. Krabs: SpongeBob, why is it taking you so long to fill the saltshakers?

SpongeBob: It's really hard getting the salt through the little holes on top.

Patrick: How much is a soda?

Mr. Krabs: A dollar.

Patrick: How much is a refill?

Mr. Krabs: It's free.

Patrick: Well then, I'll take the refill.

Sandy: SpongeBob, tell me the joke about the butter.

SpongeBob: No, you'd only spread it around.

Sandy: Then tell me the one about the egg.

SpongeBob: Oh, that one will crack you up.

Sandy: Did I tell you the one about the banana peel?

SpongeBob: No.

Sandy: It must have slipped my mind.

41

SpongeBob: You should go wash your face. I can tell what you had for breakfast today.

Patrick: Oh, yeah? What did I have for breakfast today?

SpongeBob: Oatmeal.

Patrick: Sorry, you're wrong. That was yesterday.

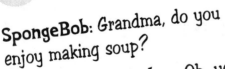

SpongeBob: Grandma, do you enjoy making soup?

SpongeBob's Grandma: Oh, yes. It is a stirring experience.

Cracked Up Cookbooks

Sweet Treats
by Candy Kane

Picnic Favorites
by Frank Furter

The Big Book of Pizza Toppings
by Anne Chovey, Tom Maito, and Mead Ball

Nutty Knock-Knocks

Knock, knock.
Who's there?
Pecan.
Pecan who?
Pecan someone
your own size!

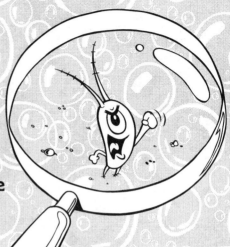

Knock, knock.
Who's there?
Justin.
Justin who?
Justin time for
Krabby Patties.

Knock, knock.
Who's there?
Doughnut
Doughnut who?
Doughnut open till Christmas.

Knock, knock.
Who's there?
Duncan.
Duncan who?
Duncan cookies in
milk is yummy.

Knock, knock.
Who's there?
Ice-cream soda.
Ice-cream soda who?
Ice-scream soda people in
Bikini Bottom can hear me.

Knock, knock.
Who's there?
Lettuce.
Lettuce who?
Lettuce stop telling
these jokes already!